presents

GIGANOTOSAURUS

THE GIANT SOUTHERN LIZARD!

ILLUSTRATED BY TERRY RILEY

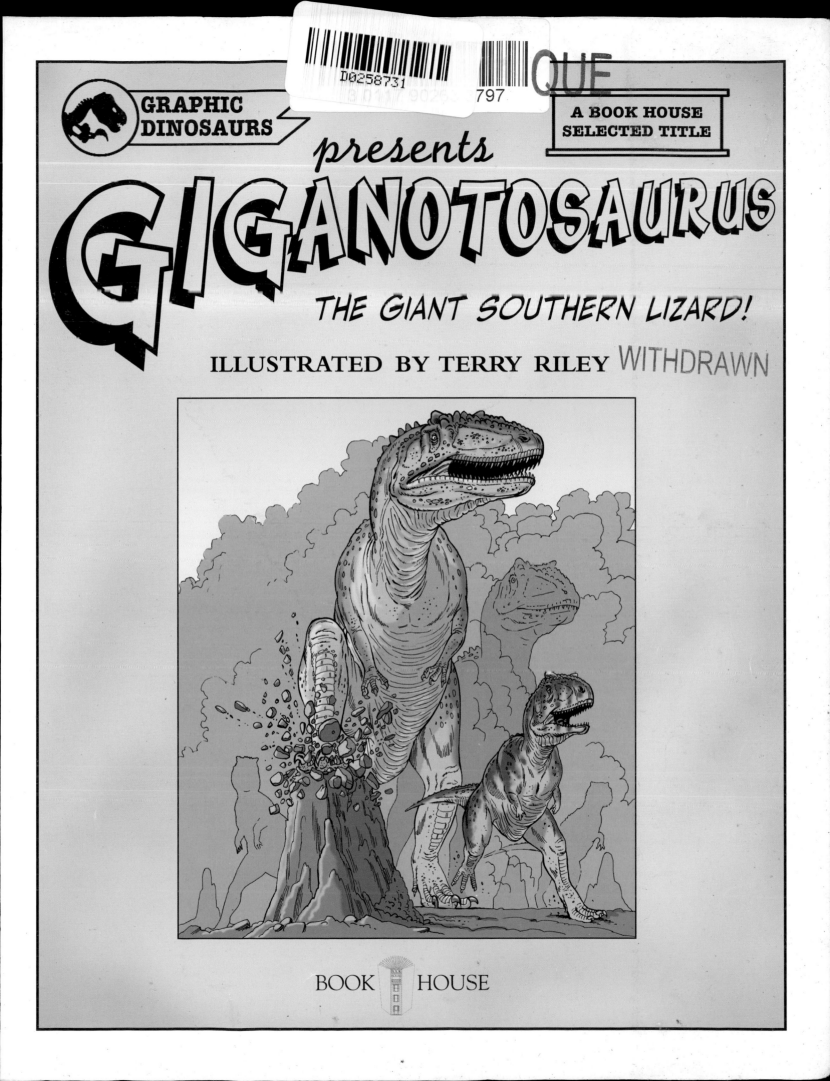

BOOK HOUSE

Graphic Dinosaurs Giganotosaurus
was produced by
David West Children's Books
7 Princeton Court
55 Felsham Road
London SW15 1AZ

Designed and written by Rob Shone
Illustrated by Terry Riley
Consultant: Steve Parker, Senior Scientific Fellow, Zoological Society of London
Cover designed by Rob Walker

First published in the UK in MMXII by Book House,
an imprint of The Salariya Book Company Ltd.,
25, Marlborough Place, Brighton BN1 1UB

Please visit the Salariya Book Company at:
www.book-house.co.uk

1 3 5 7 9 8 6 4 2

ISBN: 978-1-908177-74-2 (HB)
ISBN: 978-1-908177-47-6 (PB)

A CIP catalogue record for this book is available from the British Library.

Photographic credits:
5t, Jeff Kubina; 5b, istockphoto.com/John Pitcher; 30, Alessandro Abate.

Printed and bound in China.

CONTENTS

WHAT IS A GIGANOTOSAURUS?

GIGANOTOSAURUS MEANS 'GIANT SOUTHERN LIZARD'

← *Giganotosaurus had a good sense of smell to help it sniff out its* **prey**.

← *Giganotosaurus teeth were long and flat. Both their front and back edges were serrated, like steak knives. This made it easier to cut through meat.*

← *Giganotosaurus used its tail to counter-balance the mass of its huge head and body, like one side of a seesaw.*

← *Its heavy body was supported on two strong legs.*

→ *Its eyes faced sideways. This would have made it hard to judge distances.*

→ *For such a large animal, Giganotosaurus had a small brain. Its brain was the same size and shape as a banana.*

→ *Giganotosaurus had short arms and three fingers on each hand. It used them to grab hold of its prey.*

GIGANOTOSAURUS WAS A DINOSAUR THAT LIVED AROUND 95 MILLION TO 90 MILLION YEARS AGO, DURING THE **CRETACEOUS PERIOD**. FOSSILS OF ITS SKELETON HAVE BEEN FOUND IN SOUTH AMERICA.

An adult Giganotosaurus measured up to 13 metres long, 4 metres high, and weighed around 5,400 kilogrammes.

Giganotosaurus had a 2-metre skull and 76 teeth, each one 20 centimetres long.

SHARP TEETH

Giganotosaurus's teeth were long and flat with serrated edges, like a steak knife. The teeth cut as they bit down and cut again as they pulled back from the prey. Giganotosauruses took bite after bite out of a **sauropod** victim. Finally the sauropod would lose so much blood it would die.

Great white shark teeth (left) have serrated edges like Giganotosaurus teeth.

AIRHEADS

Giganotosaurus had a very long and narrow head. It was not heavy, though. Its skull had holes in it which made it light but still strong enough to attack its prey.

Giganotosauruses may have lived and hunted in family groups (see page 30), just as African lions do.

PART ONE... THE ORPHANS

THE GIGANOTOSAURUS HAS BEEN DEAD FOR THREE DAYS. A PAIR OF CARNOTAURUSES WALK SLOWLY TOWARD THE BODY. THEY SEE THE CHANCE TO **SCAVENGE** A MEAL.

THE GIGANOTOSAURUS HAD BEEN WEAKENED BY DISEASE AND INJURY. UNABLE TO KEEP UP WITH THE PACK, SHE HAD RESTED AND DIED.

HIDING BY HER MASSIVE BODY ARE THREE ONE-MONTH-OLD HATCHLINGS. THEY HAVE NOT LEFT THEIR MOTHER'S SIDE. BUT THE CARNOTAURUSES ARE MAKING THEM NERVOUS.

AS THE CARNOTAURUSES GET CLOSER AND CLOSER, THE HATCHLINGS STAY AS STILL AS THEY CAN.

THE UNENLAGIAS CHASE ONE OF THE HATCHLINGS.

THEY CAN RUN FASTER THAN THE SMALL GIGANOTOSAURUS.

JUST BEFORE HE IS CAUGHT...

...THE HATCHLING FINDS A HIDING PLACE.

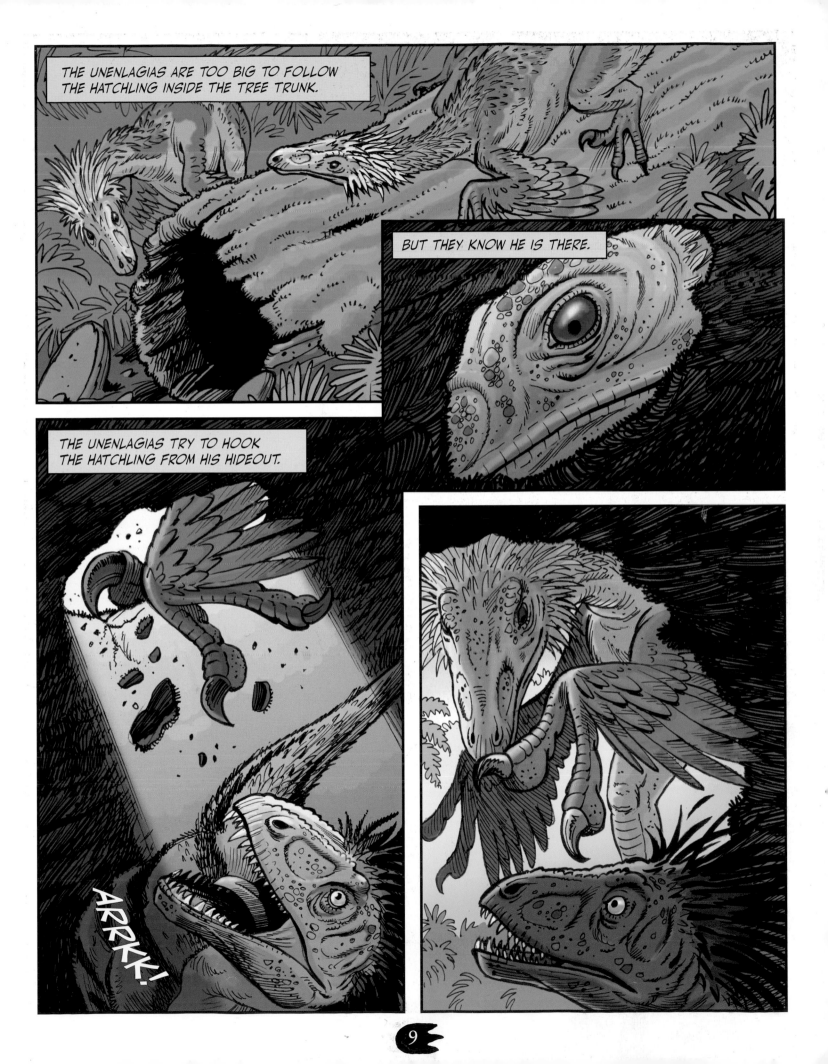

THE UNENLAGIAS ARE TOO BIG TO FOLLOW THE HATCHLING INSIDE THE TREE TRUNK.

BUT THEY KNOW HE IS THERE.

THE UNENLAGIAS TRY TO HOOK THE HATCHLING FROM HIS HIDEOUT.

ARRKK!

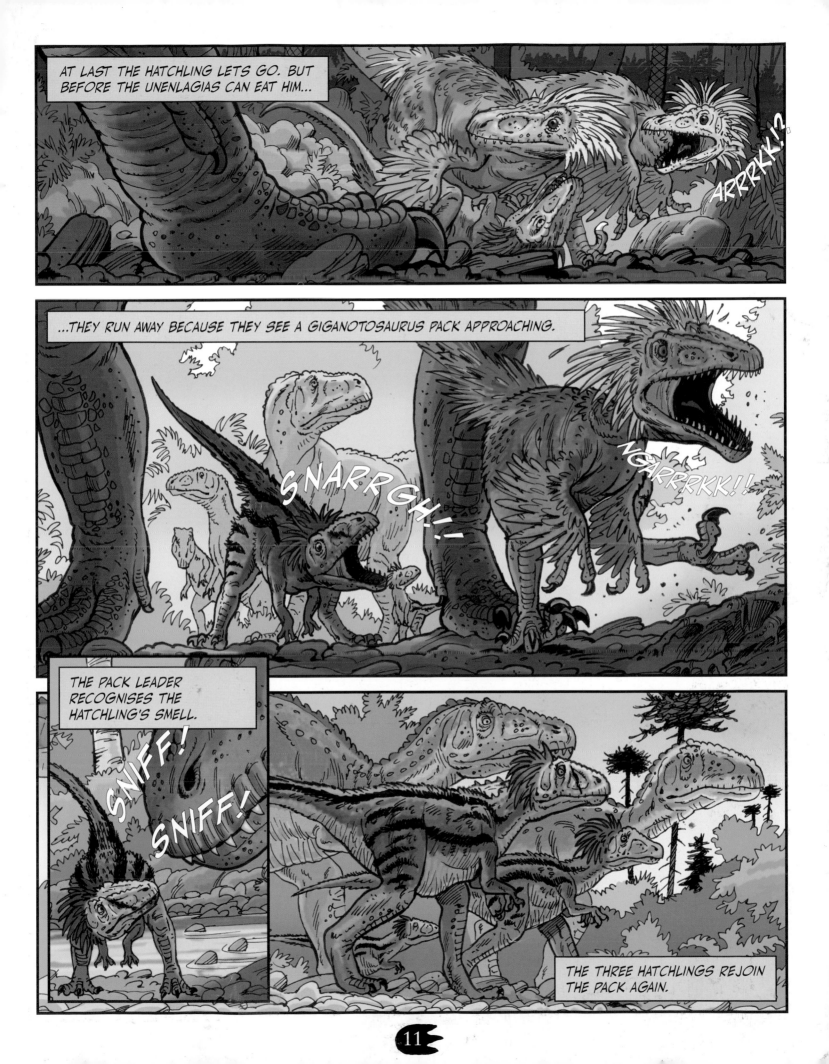

PART TWO... LESSONS

SCARFACE, THE HATCHLING THAT HAD FOUGHT THE UNENLAGIA, IS NOW TWO YEARS OLD. HE ONLY HAS ONE BROTHER LEFT.

THEY ARE TOO SMALL TO HUNT WITH THE PACK, SO SCARFACE AND HIS BROTHER PRACTICE THEIR HUNTING SKILLS IN THE FOREST.

THEY PASS A GROUP OF GASPARINISAURAS. THOSE TINY PLANT EATERS ARE IN NO DANGER. THE GIGANOTOSAURUSES HAVE PICKED UP THE SCENT OF SOMETHING BIGGER.

THEY HAVE TRACKED DOWN A PAIR OF **JUVENILE** PATAGONYKUSES. THEY WILL TRY TO GET AS CLOSE AS THEY CAN BEFORE AMBUSHING THE INSECT EATERS.

THE PATAGONYKUSES ARE USING THEIR LARGE FRONT CLAWS TO SEARCH FOR BUGS THAT LIVE UNDER THE TREE BARK. THEY DO NOT KNOW THAT THE GIGANOTOSAURUSES ARE **STALKING** THEM.

CRACKKK!!

THE PATAGONYKUSES HEAR THE SOUND OF A TWIG BEING BROKEN. IT HAS MADE THEM JUMPY.

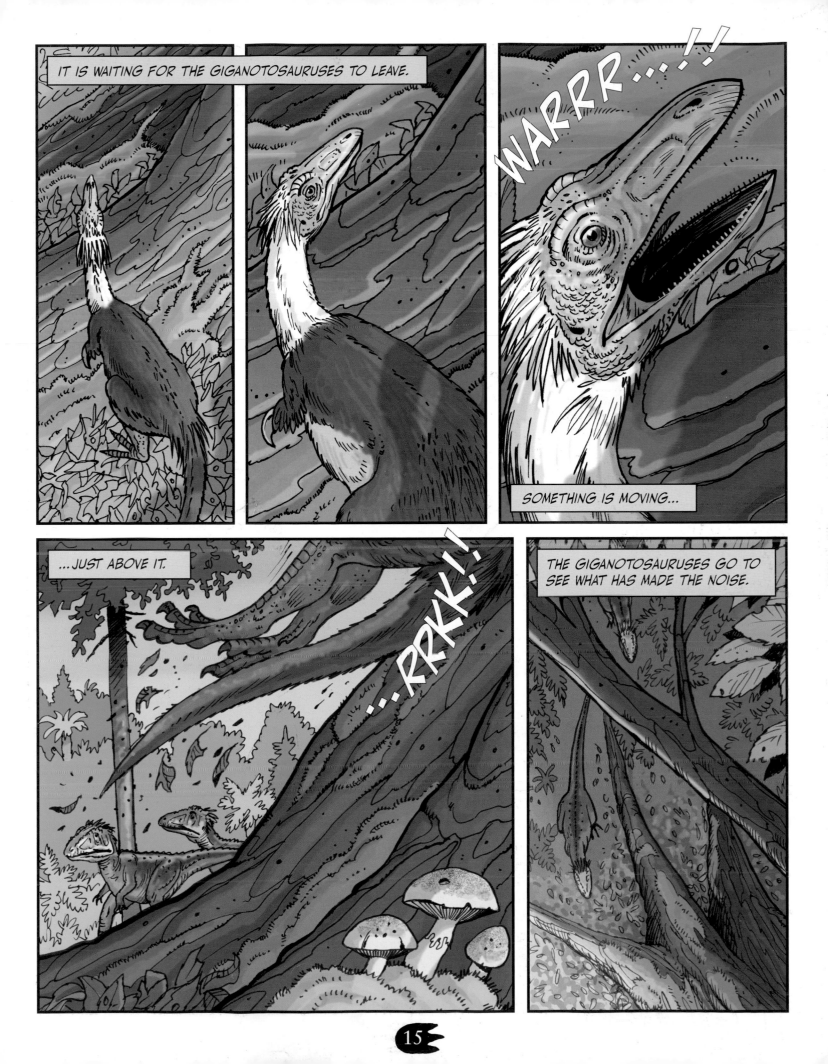

BUT THE SNAKE COILS ITS TAIL AROUND SCARFACE'S BODY

THE SNAKE COILS AROUND THE GIGANOTOSAURUS AGAIN. SCARFACE CANNOT MOVE.

SZCHAHHH!!!

BUT THE PATAGONYKUS IS NOT DEAD. IT TRIES TO FREE ITSELF.

ARRK! ARRK!!

WHILE THE SNAKE IS TRYING TO CONTROL THE STRUGGLING PATAGONYKUS, SCARFACE MANAGES TO ESCAPE FROM ITS GRIP.

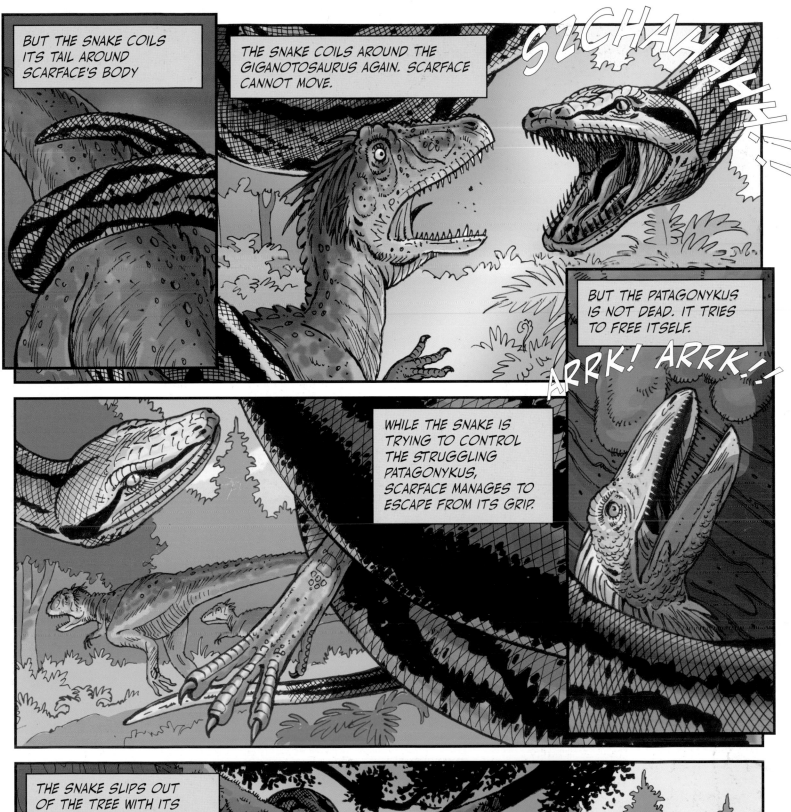

THE SNAKE SLIPS OUT OF THE TREE WITH ITS PREY. SCARFACE AND HIS BROTHER ARE NOT BIG ENOUGH TO TAKE THE PATAGONYKUS FROM THE GIANT REPTILE. MAYBE THE GASPARINISAURAS ARE STILL IN THE FOREST. THE HUNGRY DINOSAURS RUSH BACK TO WHERE THEY LAST SAW THEM.

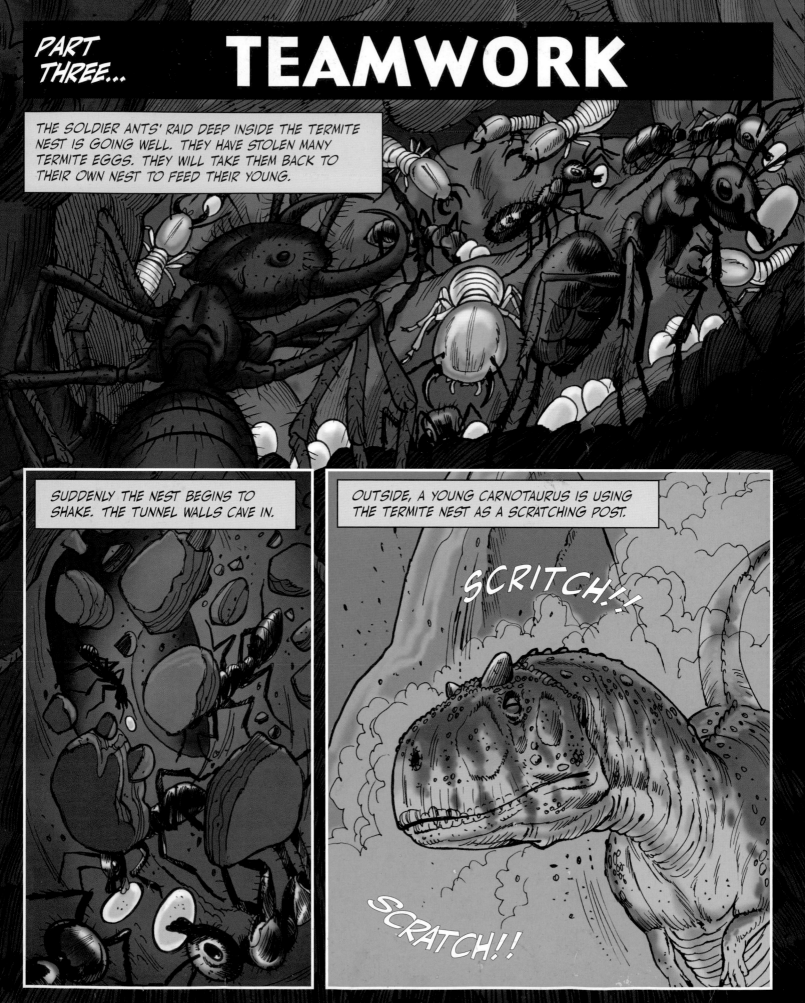

PART THREE... TEAMWORK

THE SOLDIER ANTS' RAID DEEP INSIDE THE TERMITE NEST IS GOING WELL. THEY HAVE STOLEN MANY TERMITE EGGS. THEY WILL TAKE THEM BACK TO THEIR OWN NEST TO FEED THEIR YOUNG.

SUDDENLY THE NEST BEGINS TO SHAKE. THE TUNNEL WALLS CAVE IN.

OUTSIDE, A YOUNG CARNOTAURUS IS USING THE TERMITE NEST AS A SCRATCHING POST.

SCRITCH!!

SCRATCH!!

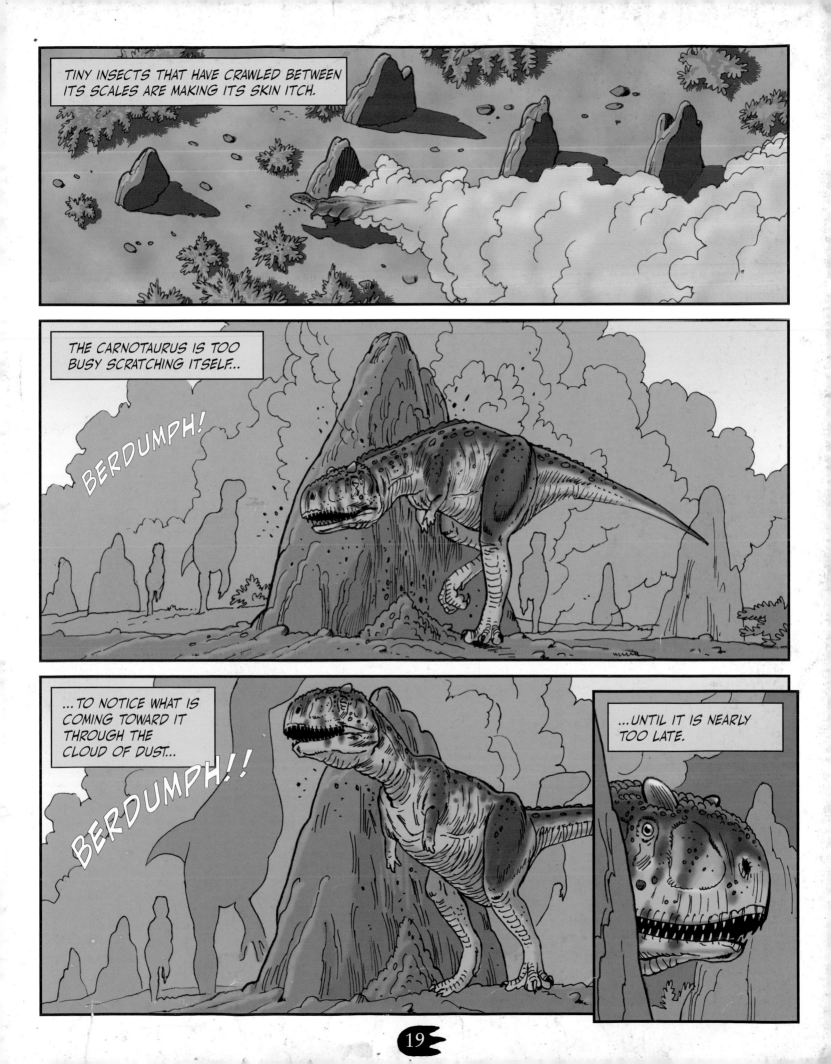

TINY INSECTS THAT HAVE CRAWLED BETWEEN ITS SCALES ARE MAKING ITS SKIN ITCH.

THE CARNOTAURUS IS TOO BUSY SCRATCHING ITSELF...

BERDUMPH!

...TO NOTICE WHAT IS COMING TOWARD IT THROUGH THE CLOUD OF DUST...

BERDUMPH!!

...UNTIL IT IS NEARLY TOO LATE.

THE CARNOTAURUS RUNS AS FAST AS IT CAN WHEN IT SEES THE GIGANOTOSAURUSES. BUT THEY ARE NOT INTERESTED IN THE SMALL MEAT EATER. THEY ARE CHASING SOMETHING MUCH LARGER, A HERD OF ARGENTINOSAURUSES.

BERKERRUMPHH!!

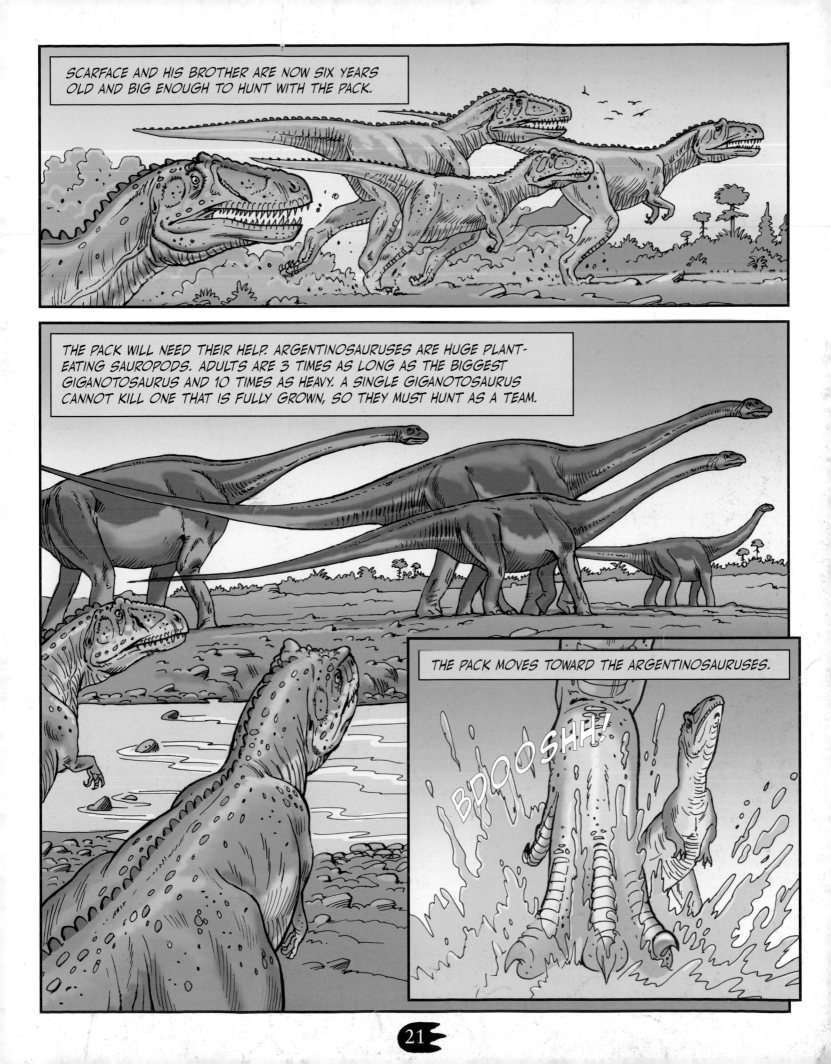

SCARFACE AND HIS BROTHER ARE NOW SIX YEARS OLD AND BIG ENOUGH TO HUNT WITH THE PACK.

THE PACK WILL NEED THEIR HELP. ARGENTINOSAURUSES ARE HUGE PLANT-EATING SAUROPODS. ADULTS ARE 3 TIMES AS LONG AS THE BIGGEST GIGANOTOSAURUS AND 10 TIMES AS HEAVY. A SINGLE GIGANOTOSAURUS CANNOT KILL ONE THAT IS FULLY GROWN, SO THEY MUST HUNT AS A TEAM.

THE PACK MOVES TOWARD THE ARGENTINOSAURUSES.

BDOOSHH!

THE ARGENTINOSAURUS HERD STAYS CLOSE TOGETHER. THE YOUNG ARE EASY TO KILL, SO THEY ARE IN THE MIDDLE, GUARDED BY THE HUGE ADULTS. THE ADULTS ARE DANGEROUS TO ATTACK, EVEN FOR A GIGANOTOSAURUS PACK. BUT THEY HAVE SPOTTED AN OLD AND SICK MEMBER OF THE HERD. THEY WILL TRY TO SEPARATE IT FROM THE OTHERS.

SCARFACE AND HIS BROTHER ARE AT THE FRONT OF THE ARGENTINOSAURUS HERD. THEY ARE TRYING TO GET IT TO RUN QUICKLY SO THAT THE WEAK ONE IS LEFT BEHIND.

SCARFACE'S BROTHER DOES NOT SEE THAT THERE IS A HOLE IN THE PATH AHEAD.

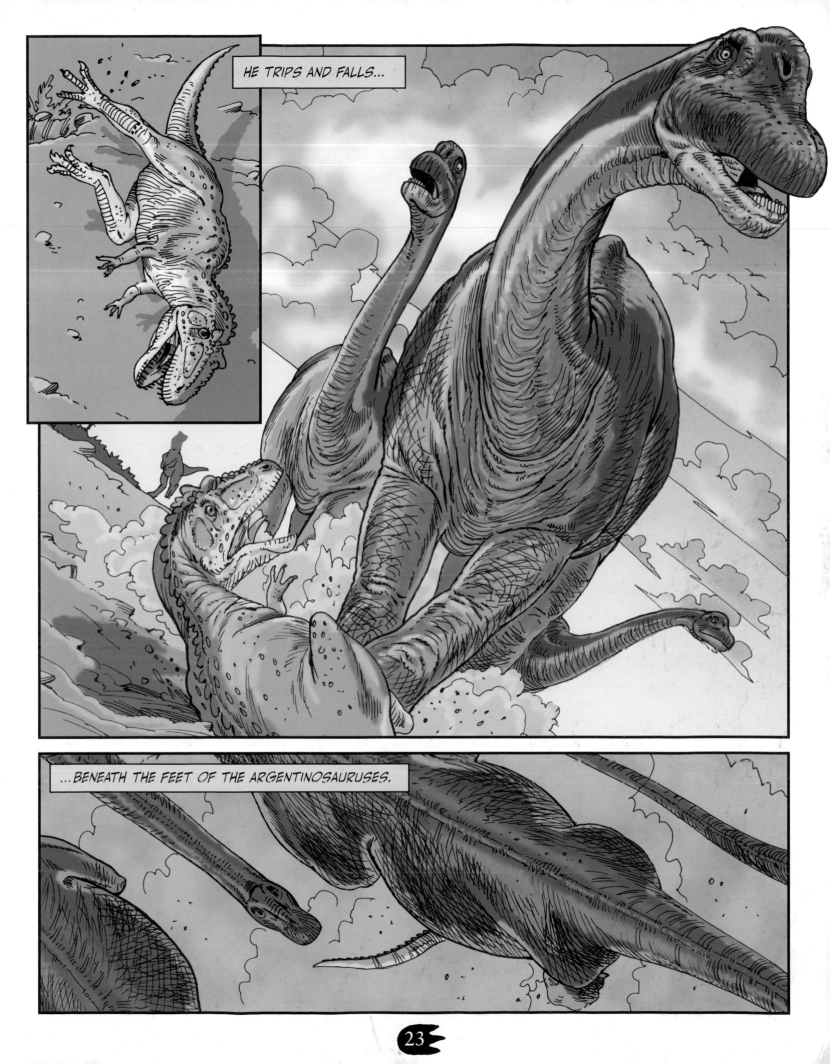

HE TRIPS AND FALLS...

...BENEATH THE FEET OF THE ARGENTINOSAURUSES.

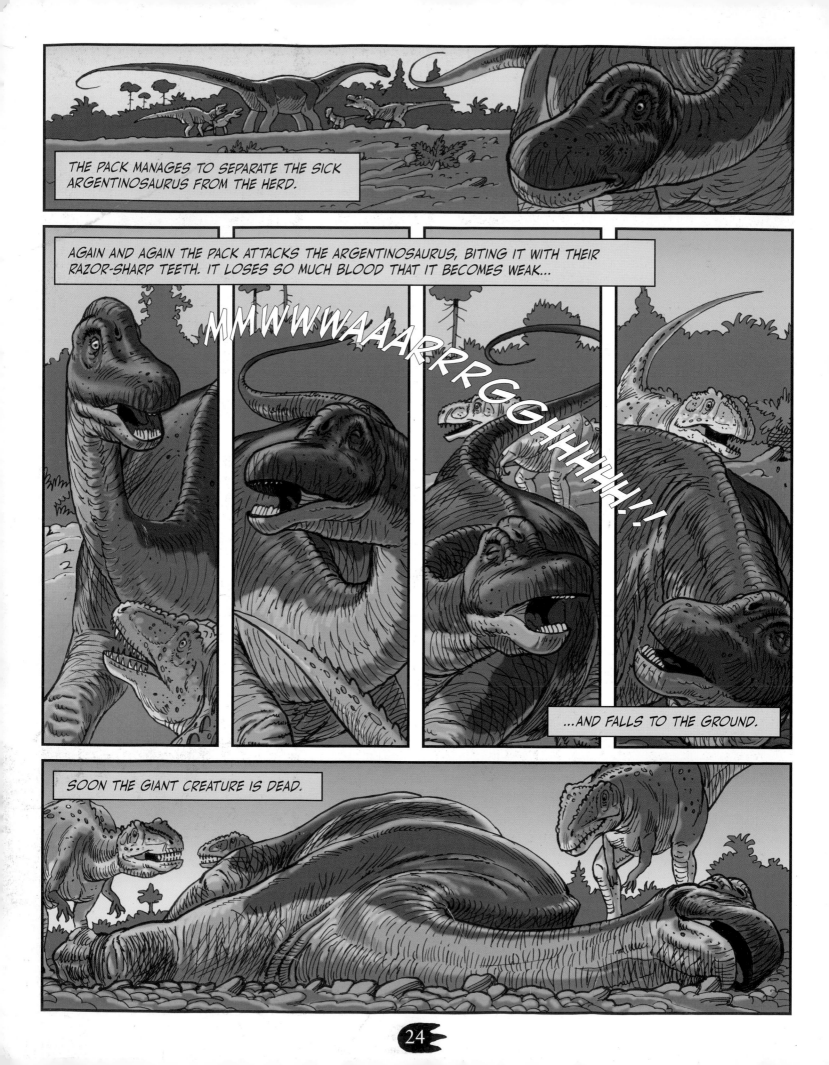

THE PACK MANAGES TO SEPARATE THE SICK ARGENTINOSAURUS FROM THE HERD.

AGAIN AND AGAIN THE PACK ATTACKS THE ARGENTINOSAURUS, BITING IT WITH THEIR RAZOR-SHARP TEETH. IT LOSES SO MUCH BLOOD THAT IT BECOMES WEAK...

MMWWWAAARRGGHHHH!!

...AND FALLS TO THE GROUND.

SOON THE GIANT CREATURE IS DEAD.

THE PACK FEEDS GREEDILY ON THE DEAD ANIMAL. SCARFACE IS TOO HUNGRY TO NOTICE HIS BROTHER IS MISSING.

NEARBY, THE YOUNG CARNOTAURUS WATCHES THE GIGANOTOSAURUSES. IT IS HOPING THERE WILL BE SOME FOOD LEFT WHEN THE PACK LEAVES. THAT WILL NOT BE FOR MANY DAYS, THOUGH. IT WILL COME BACK LATER.

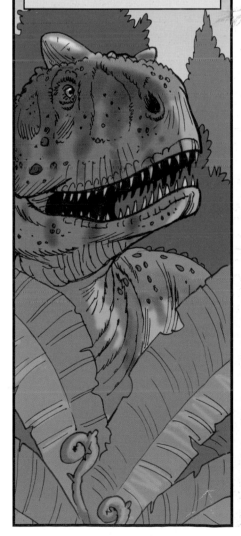

MEANWHILE, THE TINY INSECTS ARE MAKING ITS SKIN ITCH AGAIN. IT NEEDS TO FIND ANOTHER TERMITE NEST TO SCRATCH AGAINST.

THE SOLDIER ANTS ARE MARCHING BACK TO THEIR NEST CARRYING THEIR TERMITE EGGS.

PART FOUR

LEADERS

THE GIGANOTOSAURUSES HAVE KILLED A YOUNG ARGENTINOSAURUS. THE PACK FEEDS ON IT EVEN THOUGH A STORM IS COMING. SCARFACE IS NOW 12 YEARS OLD AND AN ADULT. THE PACK'S LEADER IS A LARGE FEMALE.

THE SMELL OF THE KILL HAS DRAWN A SMALL PACK OF MAPUSAURUSES. THEIR LEADER IS A HUGE MALE, BIGGER THAN ANY OF THE GIGANOTOSAURUSES. THEY WANT TO STEAL THE PACK'S KILL. THE BIG MAPUSAURUS ROARS OUT A CHALLENGE TO THE GIGANOTOSAURUSES.

WARRRGHH!!

THE GIGANOTOSAURUS LEADER WILL NOT LET THE MAPUSAURUSES HAVE THE SAUROPOD WITHOUT A FIGHT.

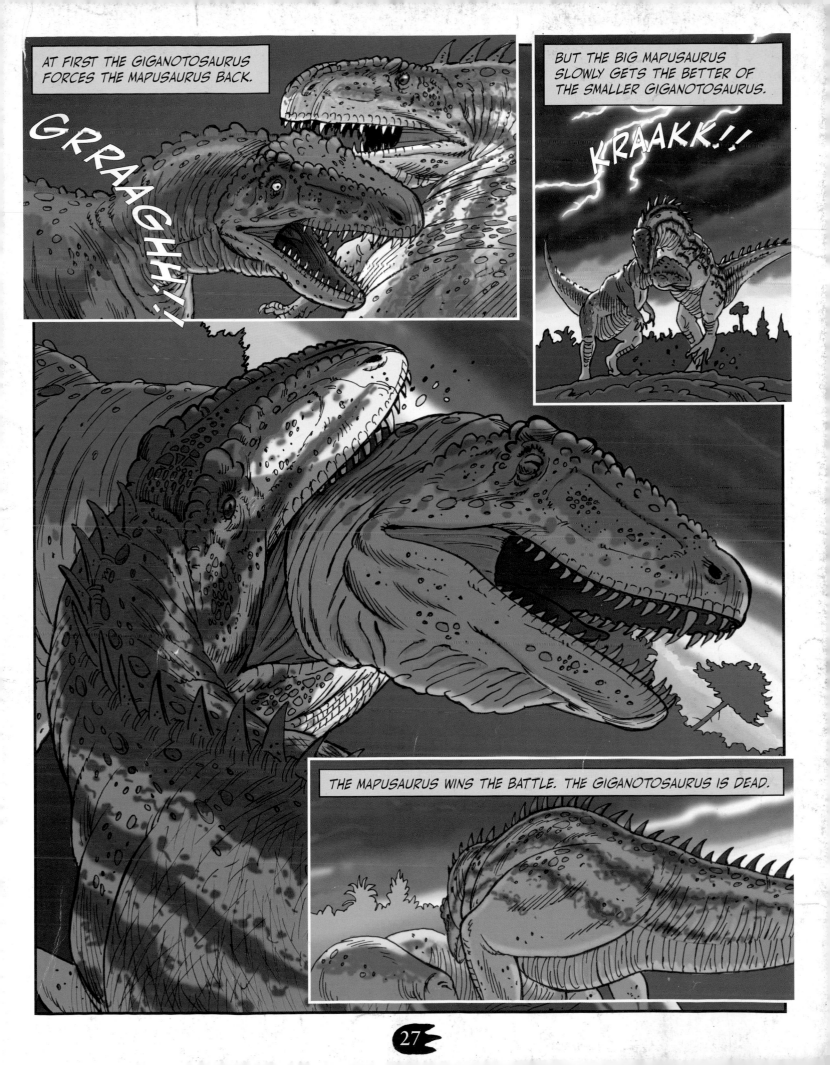

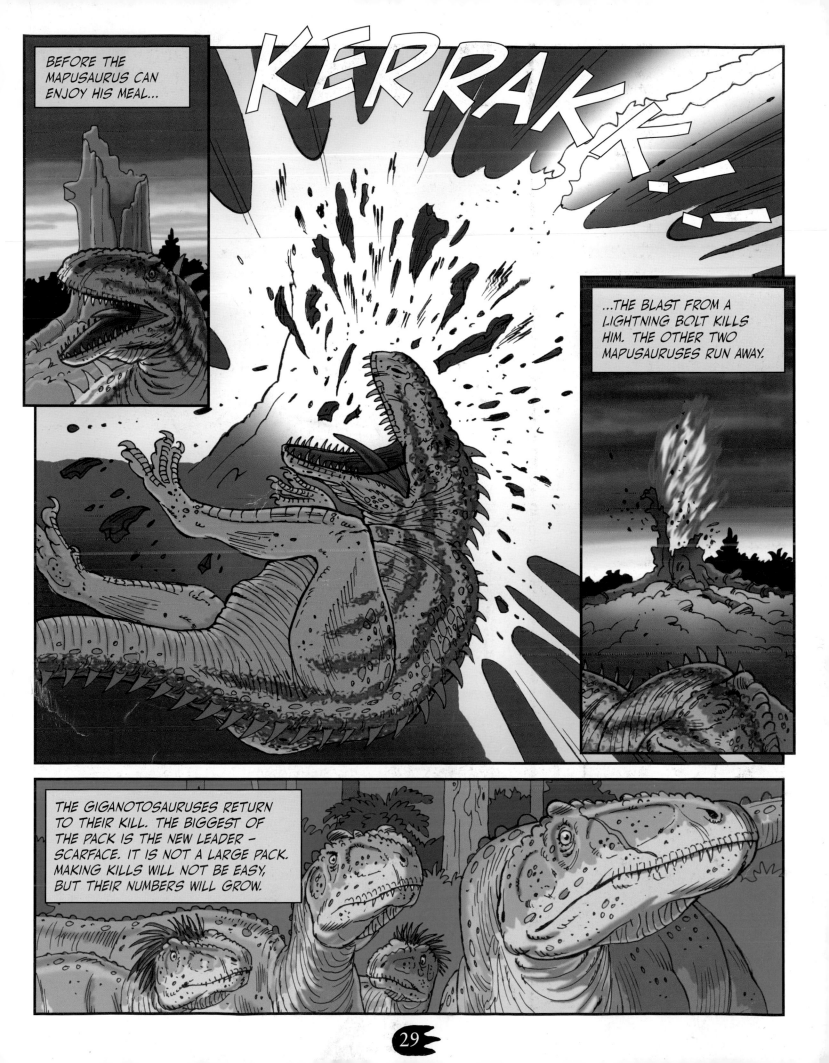

BEFORE THE MAPUSAURUS CAN ENJOY HIS MEAL...

KERRAKK!!

...THE BLAST FROM A LIGHTNING BOLT KILLS HIM. THE OTHER TWO MAPUSAURUSES RUN AWAY.

THE GIGANOTOSAURUSES RETURN TO THEIR KILL. THE BIGGEST OF THE PACK IS THE NEW LEADER – SCARFACE. IT IS NOT A LARGE PACK. MAKING KILLS WILL NOT BE EASY, BUT THEIR NUMBERS WILL GROW.

FOSSIL EVIDENCE

SCIENTISTS LEARN WHAT DINOSAURS MAY HAVE LOOKED LIKE BY STUDYING THEIR FOSSIL REMAINS. FOSSILS ARE FORMED WHEN THE HARD PARTS OF AN ANIMAL OR PLANT BECOME BURIED AND TURN TO ROCK OVER THOUSANDS OF YEARS.

The picture below shows a Giganotosaurus attacking a huge sauropod called an Argentinosaurus. Giganotosaurus was first found in 1993 in Argentina, South America. Near it was the fossilised skeleton of a 23-metre long sauropod. Scientists believe that these large plant-eating dinosaurs were hunted by Giganotosauruses. But the full-grown sauropods were very big.

Could a single Giganotosaurus kill an animal ten times heavier than itself? In 1997 seven fossilised Mapusauruses were found together. They had died at the same time. They may have been a family group, because there were young and old animals. As Mapusauruses were related to Giganotosauruses, both animals could have hunted the big sauropods in packs.

ANIMAL GALLERY

ALL THESE ANIMALS APPEAR IN THE STORY.

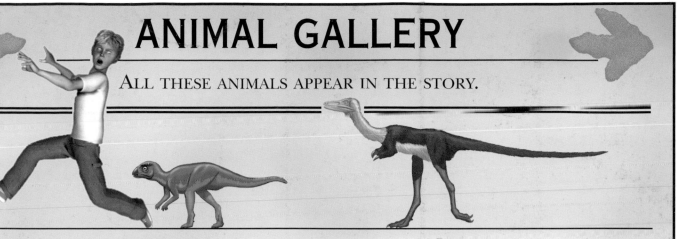

Gasparinisaura
'Gasparini's lizard'
Length: 1 metre
A small plant-eating dinosaur.

Patagonykus
'Patagonian claw'
Length: 2 metres
A small insect-eating dinosaur with one large claw at the end of each arm.

Unenlagia
'Half bird'
Length: 2.5 metres
A birdlike meat eater that had a claw on each of its first toes.

Madtsoiid snake
'Cow valley snake'
Length: 9 metres
An early type of snake that probably crushed its prey.

Carnotaurus
'Meat-eating bull'
Length: 8.5 metres
A large meat-eating dinosaur with tiny arms. It weighed 1,600 kilogrammes.

Mapusaurus
'Earth lizard'
Length: 12.5 metres
A meat-eating dinosaur that was a close relative of Giganotosaurus.

Argentinosaurus
'Argentina lizard'
Length: 25–30 metres
A giant plant-eating dinosaur weighing around 81,600 kilogrammes.

GLOSSARY

ambush	To attack from a hiding place.
Cretaceous period	The period of time between 145 million and 65 million years ago.
fossils	The remains of living things that have turned to rock.
juvenile	A young animal that is not fully grown.
prey	Animals that are hunted for food by another animal.
sauropod	Any of a group of the largest four-footed, plant-eating dinosaurs with long necks and tails and small heads.
scavenge	To search for dead animals to eat.
stalking	Secretly following someone.

INDEX